VOICES
VOICES
VOICES
VOICES

JOANNE ROBINSON MITCHELL
ANNE LIBBY RYLE

CONSULTANT MARCELLA JOHNSON

D. C. HEATH AND COMPANY

LEXINGTON, MASSACHUSETTS   TORONTO   LONDON

UNIT ONE

CONTENTS

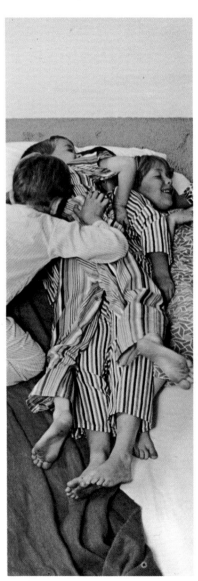

UNDER A HILL

There was an old woman
Lived under a hill,
And if she's not gone
She lives there still.

—*Mother Goose*

THE HOUSE THE KING HAD

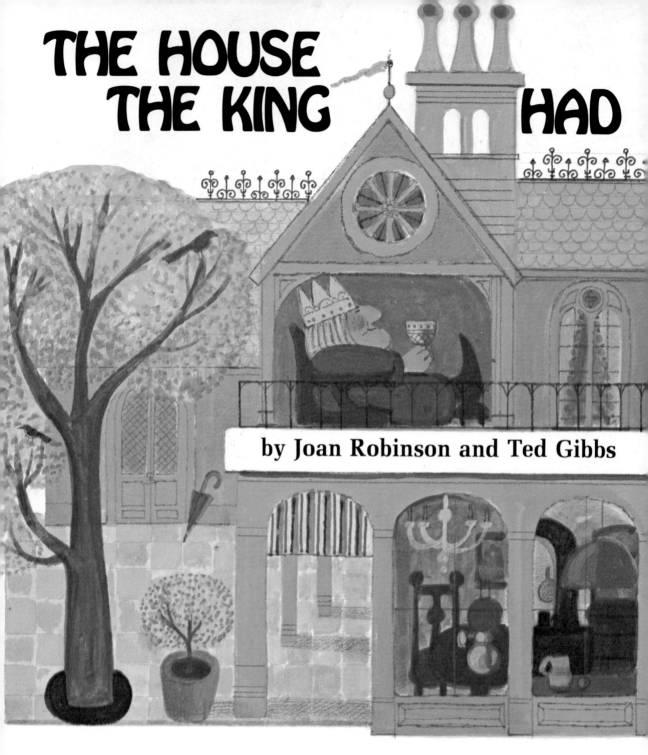

by Joan Robinson and Ted Gibbs

This is the house the king had.

This is the giant
who came to the house the king had.

This is the witch
who chased the giant
who came to the house the king had.

This is the cat,

the black, black cat,

that sat on the witch

who chased the giant

who came to the house the king had.

QUESTIONS

1. Who is this?
2. What did the witch do?
3. What did the cat do to the witch?

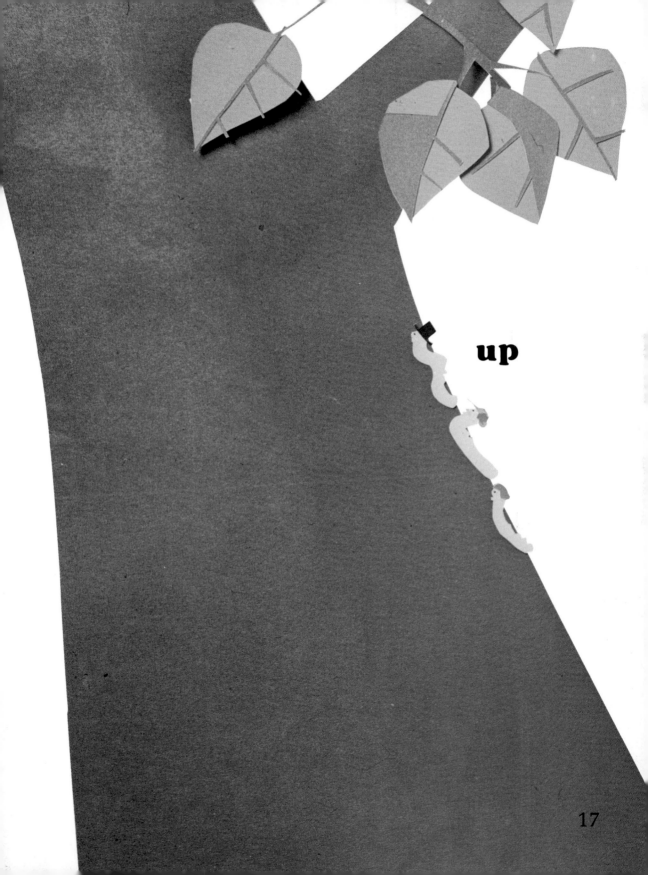

up

down

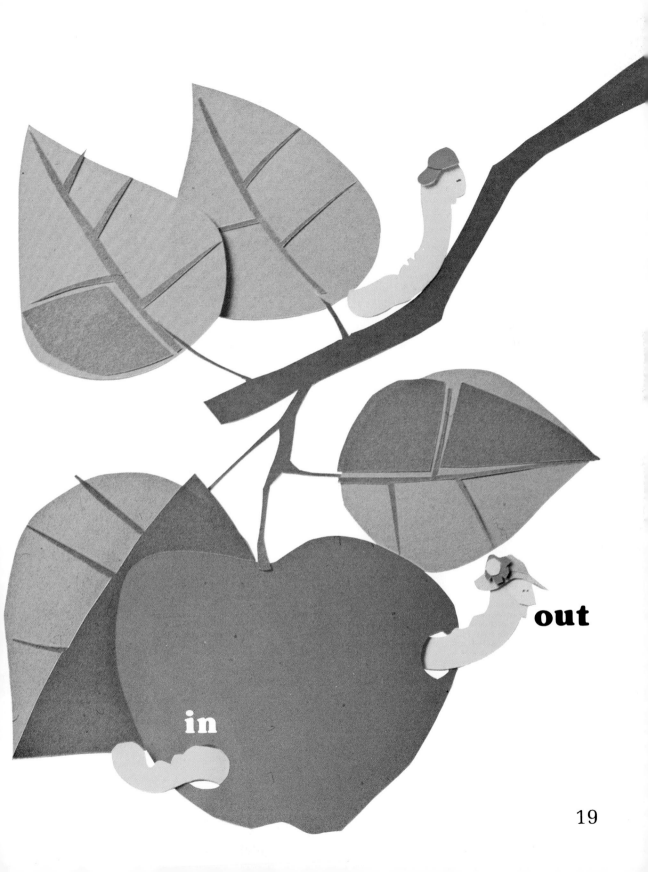

in

out

down

up

out

around

in

20

HOW TO GO UP

by Anne Morecroft

Do you want to go up?

You can go up like this.

You can go up a tree like this.
But a cat can go up a tree like this.

22

Some things
go up like this.

And some things go up like this.

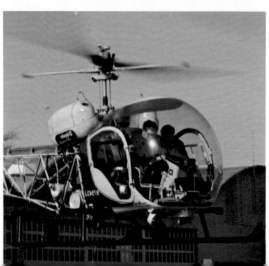

24

There are many ways to go up.

QUESTIONS

1. What goes up this way?

2. Can you go up this way?

3. Draw a picture that shows how you like to go up.

Pam: What goes up
when the rain comes down?

Sam: An umbrella.

FOR FUN JUST

Sam: I would not want this dog.

Pam: Why not?

Sam: The sign says
this dog will eat everything.
And he likes boys very much.

FUN FUN

DAN

by Joanne Mitchell

My name is Dan.

I get into everything.

I look at everything.

I eat everything.

This looks good.
It shines.

Who will know
if I eat one?

Mmm. That was good.
I could eat one more.

Just one more.

Dan! What did you do?

Where did they go?

Did you eat them all?

You cannot eat things that shine.

They are not good for you.

Now I do not eat everything.

30

I do not eat things
that shine.

QUESTIONS

1. Who got into everything?

2. Will Dan eat this
   any more?

3. Draw a picture to show
   what might happen next.

NO PETS

by Nomi Waldman

"Can we have a pet?" asked Jill.

"No pets," said Dad.

"No pets," said Mom.

"You would not look
after it," said Dad.

"Yes we would," said David.

"You do not look after your things
now," said Mom.

"What can we do?"
asked David.

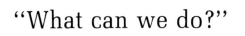

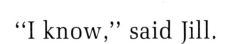

"I know," said Jill.

"Come on, little cat,"
said David and Jill.
"We have work to do."

"See," said David.

"We do look after our things."

"And we will look after our cat too," said Jill.

"Your cat?" said Dad.

"Do you have a cat?" asked Mom.

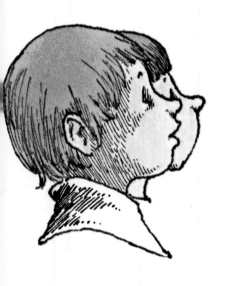

"We did," said David and Jill.

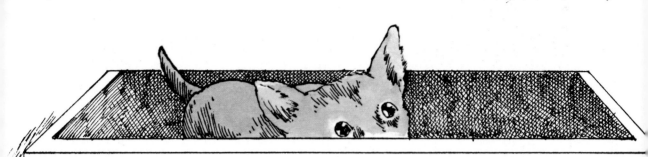

"Here is your cat," said Mom.
"You looked after him too well."

QUESTIONS

1. Who wanted a pet?
2. Why did Mom and Dad say, "No pets"?
3. What did David and Jill do to get a pet?

UNIT TWO

UNIT TWO UNIT TWO

TWO

UNIT TWO UNIT TWO

THE PIE

Who made the pie?

I did.

Who stole the pie?

He did.

Who found the pie?
She did.
Who ate the pie?
You did.
Who cried for the pie?
We all did.

—*Mother Goose*

43

THE LITTLE RED HEN

by Ann Moore

 Storyteller

 Little Red Hen

 Dog

 Pig

 Turkey

44

Once there was a little red hen.
She saw it was time to eat.

 Who wants to eat?

 I do.

 I do.

 I do. I want to eat.

Who will get the vegetables?

 Not I.

 Not I.

 Not I. That is no fun.

 Then I will.
I will get all the vegetables.

 Who will get the meat?

 Not I.

 Not I.

 Not I. That is no fun.

 Then I will do it.
I will get the meat.

Who will make something to eat?

 Not I.

 Not I.

 Not I. That is no fun.

 Then I will.

I will make something to eat.

Then it was time to eat.

 Who wants to eat?

 I want something to eat.

 I want something to eat.

 I want something to eat.
That would be fun.

 I got the vegetables.
I got the meat.
I made something to eat.
And now it is mine.
I will eat it all.

 And she did.

QUESTIONS

1. What did the turkey say when it
    was time to get the vegetables?

2. What did the turkey say when it was
    time to get the meat?

3. What did the turkey say when it was
    time to eat?

Maytime Magic

A little seed
For me to sow . . .

A little earth
To make it grow . . .
A little hole,
A little pat . . .
A little wish,
And that is that.

A little sun,
A little shower . . .
A little while,
And then—a flower!

—*Mabel Watts*

The Flower

by Rose Sommer

"I do not think it will come up,"
said her mother.

"I do not think it will come up,"
said her father.

"Oh boy!" said her brother.

54

The little girl worked hard.

But nothing came up.

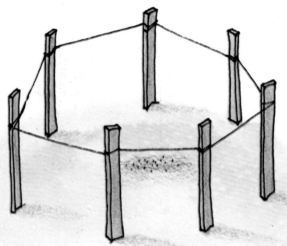

And nothing came up.

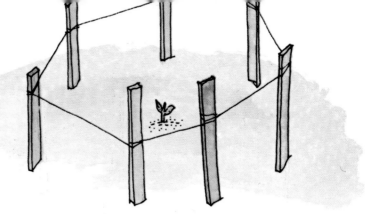

Then one day something came up.

It came up

and up and up.

QUESTIONS

1. Who said, "I do not think it will come up"?

2. Why do you think the flower came up?

3. How do you think the little girl felt when the flower came up?

Sam: Mom, may I have a dime?
It is for the lady
who is crying outside.

Mom: What is the lady crying for?

Sam: She is crying, "Ice cream."

Sam: What four letters could end a game
of hide and seek?

Pam: O-I-C-U.

Pam: What key does not open a door?

Sam: A tur*key*.

The Animals' Apartment House
by Susan Kelway

Many animals live in trees.

Sometimes many animals live

in the same tree.

This tree is just like an apartment house.

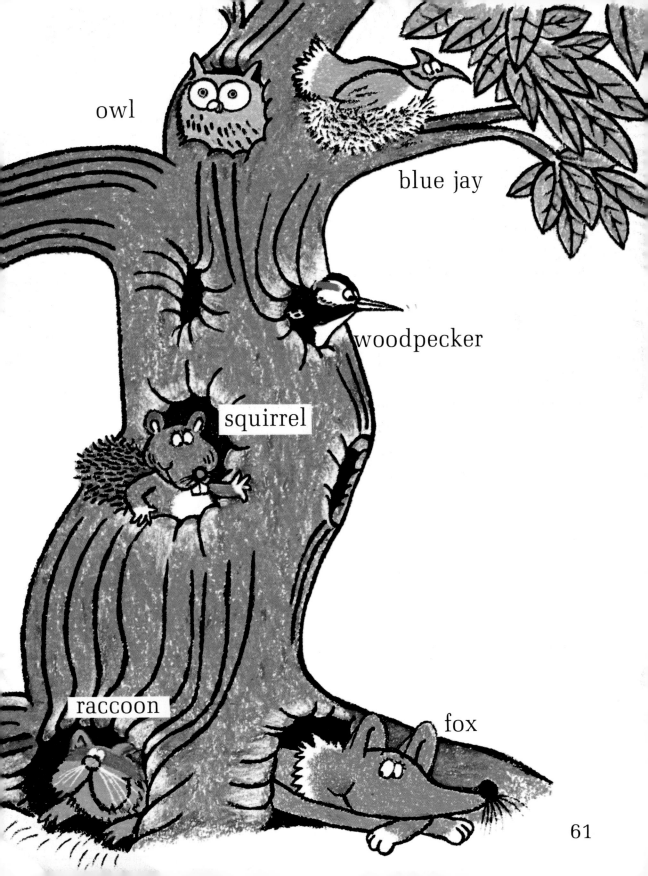

owl

blue jay

woodpecker

squirrel

raccoon

fox

61

QUESTIONS

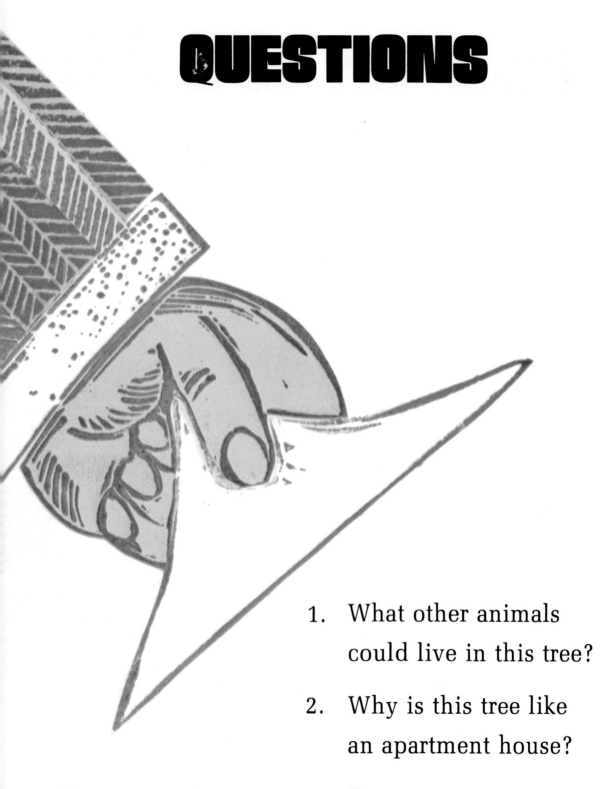

1. What other animals could live in this tree?

2. Why is this tree like an apartment house?

TEN IN A BED

by Jeanne Croft

10 Ten boys in a bed.
One of them said,
"I need more room."

9

Nine boys in a bed.
One of them said,
"I need more room."

Eight boys in a bed.
One of them said,
"I need more room."

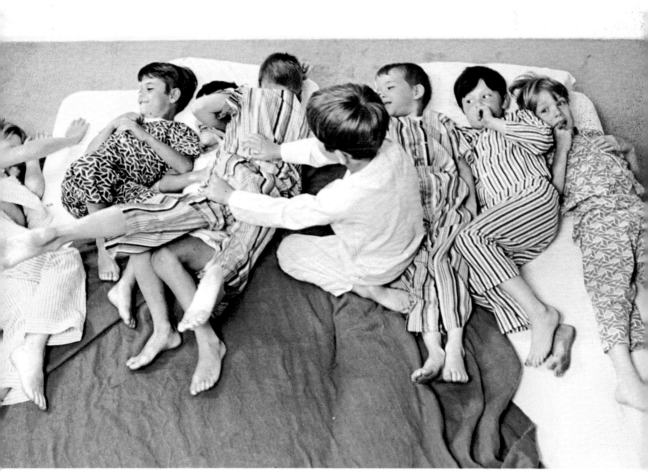

7

Seven boys in a bed.
One of them said,
"I need more room."

6 Six boys in a bed.
One of them said,
"I need more room."

 Five boys in a bed.
One of them said,
"I need more room."

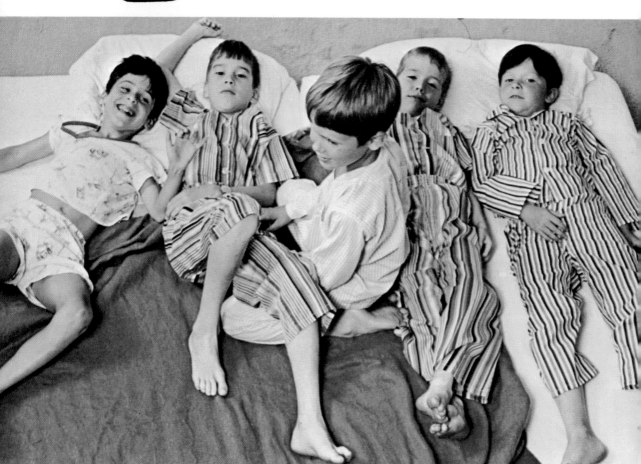

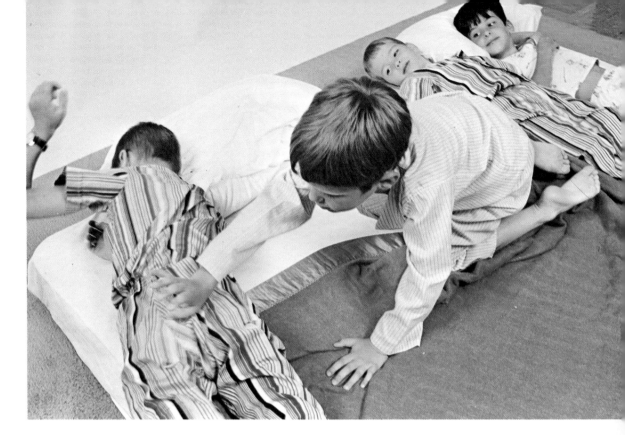

 Four boys in a bed.
One of them said,
"I need more room."

3 Three boys in a bed.
One of them said,
"I need more room."

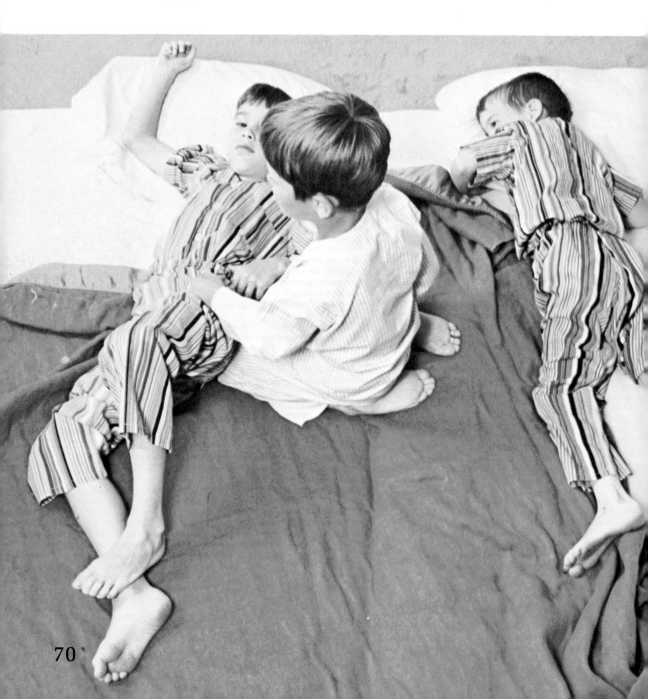

 Two boys in a bed.
One of them said,
"I need more room."

1
One boy in a bed.
He said,
"I cannot sleep.
I am all alone."

QUESTIONS

1. What did the boys
   on pages 63–71
   want?

2. What was different
   about the boy
   on page 72?

UNIT THREE

3

THREE

UNIT THREE
UNIT

SAMMY AND I

Sammy and I,
We have a date
Under the tree
By the yellow gate.

Sam said to go there.
He said, "Go at three
To the yellow gate
Under the tree."

If you are there
You will see me today
Under the tree.
We are going to play.

For Sammy and I,
We have a date
Under the tree
By the yellow gate.

—*Annie DeCaprio*

ROSA AND PEPE

by Judith Irving

Rosa and Pepe are friends.

Pepe always plays at Rosa's house.

One day Pepe called Rosa.

"I will not come to your house today,"
said Pepe. "Today is my birthday.
I asked Daddy for a boat.
I want a big blue boat.
A big blue boat will come today.

"I asked Mother for a bike.
I want a green bike.
A green bike will come today.

"I want to see my toys come.
So I will not come to your house.
Can you come to my house?"

"No," said Rosa. "You forgot.
Something is coming for me too.
It is coming today."

"What is it?" asked Pepe.

"It is something big," said Rosa.

"Is it a boat?" asked Pepe.

"No, it is not a boat," said Rosa.
"It is something big and yellow."

"Is it a bike?" asked Pepe.

"No, it is not a bike," said Rosa.
"I have to go now. It is here." 81

QUESTIONS

1. Who wanted to stay home?

2. Who was not going to stay home?

3. Why was Pepe happy?

4. How do you think Rosa felt when Pepe was talking about his new toys?

What am I?
I have teeth,
But I
cannot bite.

What am I?
I have legs,
One, two,
three, four,
But I cannot walk
Across the floor.

What am I?
I have an eye,
But
I cannot see.

A comb.

A chair.

A needle.

by Lisa Paulsen

SOMETHING FOR THE KING

by Anne Ryle

Once there was a king.
The king liked to sing.
He liked to sing every day.

Every day a man came.
The man had something
for the king to sing.

91

One day the man came.
He did not have anything
for the king to sing.
"I just have these
little things," he said.

"I cannot sing
these little things,"
said the king.

"I want something to sing.
Who can make something
for me to sing?
I will give all this
for something to sing."

A woman was in the back.
She made clothes for the king.

"I can do it," she said.
"I can make anything.
I will make something
for the king to sing."

She went to the king.

"I can make something
for you to sing," she said.

She worked all day.
She made something
for the king to sing.

Now the king was happy.
"I can sing now," he said.
"And I will give you this.
All this is for you."

QUESTIONS

1. Why was the king sad?

2. What did the king want?

3. Who made the king happy?

GO, PIG, GO

by J. Adley Robinson and
Carolyn Bamber

An old woman went to get a pig.

But the pig would not go.

"What can I do?" said the old woman.

She saw a dog.

"Dog! Dog! bite the pig.

The pig will not go.

And I cannot get home."

But the dog would not.

She saw a stick.

"Stick! Stick! hit the dog.

The dog will not bite the pig.

The pig will not go.

And I cannot get home."

So the stick began to hit the dog.

The dog began to bite the pig.

The pig began to go.

And the old woman got home that day.

QUESTIONS

1. What did the woman want the pig to do?
2. Why did the woman want the pig to go?
3. What made the dog bite the pig?
4. What helped the woman get home?

ON THE NING NANG NONG

On the Ning Nang Nong

Where the cows go Bong!

And the monkeys all say Boo!

There's a Nong Nang Ning

Where the trees go Ping!

And the teapots Jibber Jabber Joo.

On the Nong Ning Nang

All the mice go Clang!

And you just can't catch 'em when they do!

So it's Ning Nang Nong!

Cows go Bong!

Nong Nang Ning!

Trees go Ping!

Nong Ning Nang!

The mice go Clang!

What a noisy place to belong,

Is the Ning Nang Ning Nang Nong!

—*Spike Milligan*

UNIT FOUR

UNIT FOUR UNIT FOUR UNIT FOUR UNIT FOUR UNIT

Not Too Little

by Robert Morris

"Can I ride your bike?"
asked Roger.

"No," said Molly.

"Can I ride your bike?"
asked Roger.

"No," said Polly.

"Can I ride your bike?"
asked Roger.

"No," said Andy.

"Please. Can I ride
your bike?" asked Roger.
"No! You are too
little," said Dan.

"I am not too little.
I can ride a bike," said Roger.

Roger got up early the next morning.

He took Dan's bike

and rode until the sun came up.

When Dan got up, he said,
"Someone's been riding my bike.
I did not put it here."

"Maybe you forgot where you put it,"
said Andy.

"Well, maybe,"
said Dan.

Every morning Roger got up and rode
Molly's, Polly's, Andy's or Dan's bike.

Every morning Molly, Polly, Andy or
Dan said, "Someone's been riding my bike."

"What can we do?" asked Dan.

"We can hide them,"
said Polly.

Every night Molly, Polly, Andy and Dan
would hide their bikes.

Every morning Roger would find them.

And every morning
Molly, Polly, Andy or Dan said,
"Who can it be?"

One morning
they saw who it was.

"Now what do we do to keep him away
from our bikes?" asked Andy.

And this is what they did!

QUESTIONS

1. What did Roger want to do?

2. How did Roger get to ride the bike?

3. How did Molly, Polly, Andy, and Dan know someone was riding their bikes?

Linus

by Charles M. Schulz

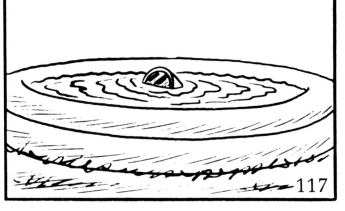

117

THE SECRET HIDING PLACE

by Rainey
Bennett

Little Hippo was the pet of the herd.
Every morning the big hippos waited
for him to wake up so they could take care
of him.

"Shush," they whispered.
"Little Hippo is sleeping."

"Quiet all!" said Big Charles.

And every morning the big hippos
pushed and bumped each other,
hurrying to bring Little Hippo
his breakfast of lily pads and corn.
Big Charles said, "Put the lily pads here
and the corn there."

Then they all settled down
to watch Little Hippo eat.

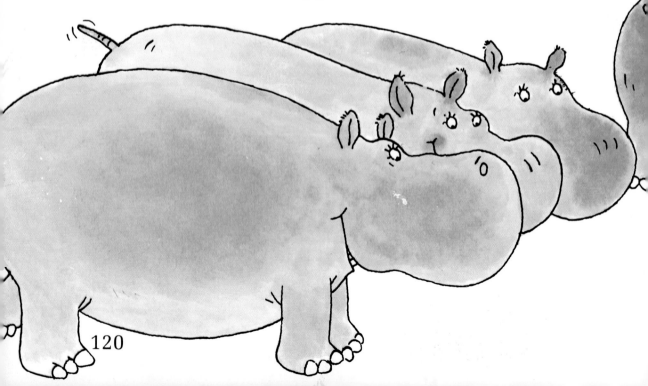

One morning Little Hippo felt cross.
"I don't want lily pads and corn,"
he grumbled. "I wish the hippos
wouldn't watch everything I do. I wish
I could be by myself once in a while."

Big Charles put a cool leaf
on Little Hippo's head
to shade him from the sun.
"Don't eat so fast," he said.

All the hippos went along
when Big Charles took Little Hippo
for his morning walk.

"We will protect you,"
said Big Charles.

But Little Hippo didn't want
to be protected. He wanted
to go exploring by himself.

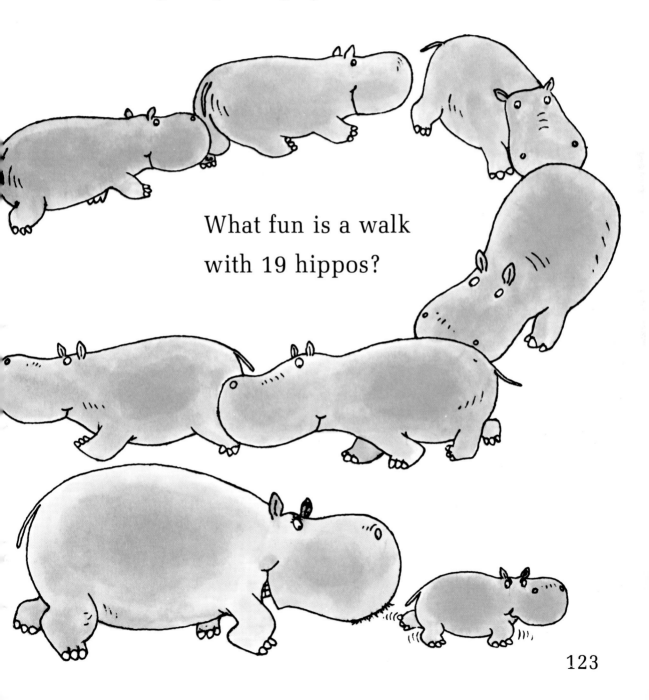

What fun is a walk
with 19 hippos?

So without even saying
"Excuse me, please,"
he dashed toward a thorny bush.

"Stop, Little Hippo!"
Big Charles bellowed.
"Birds nest there."

"Don't go in that tall grass
where zebras hide. Do you want
to catch stripes?"

Little Hippo stopped to look
at an ostrich with his head
in the sand.

"Come away, Little Hippo!"
Big Charles shouted.
"He thinks he's hiding."

When Big Charles finally caught up
with Little Hippo, he was hot
and angry.

"That's a chameleon's house,"
he puffed. "Come away this instant!"

"When will you learn not to go poking
into secret places?" Big Charles scolded.

Everyone in the jungle
had a hiding place, it seemed,
except Little Hippo.
The leopard hid in shadowy places;
the tiger chose deep grass.
Pottos curled up in trees,

and even the elephant was almost hidden
by leaves as big as his ears.

"You're lucky," Little Hippo told
the turtle and the snail.
"You carry your hiding places
with you. What's it like inside?"

"It's dark," said the turtle.

"It's dark," said the snail.

Little Hippo was still cross
at lunch (more lily pads and corn).

But later, after his nap,
there was a big surprise.

"We will play hide-and-seek,"
Big Charles said. "I will be IT."

He leaned against a tree
and started to count
to five hundred by fives.

"Now!" Little Hippo whispered.

"Now's my chance to find a hiding
place of my very own."

He raced to the flowering trees.

"Little Hippo, Little Hippo,
come hide with us."

But Little Hippo wanted his own
hiding place.

The lion laughed
when he saw Little Hippo
trying to crawl under a rock.
"Silly Hippo," he said,
"that's no place to hide.
Follow me. You can hide in my cave."

"Are we almost there?"

"Here we are," said the lion.
"Make yourself at home."

Then he went hunting
for his dinner and left Little Hippo
all alone.

The dark cave was filled
with bat squeals and wind noises.

"I'm scared," said Little Hippo.
"I don't want to be alone this much."

Little Hippo was so frightened
that he ran out of the cave
without looking where he was going—
and fell on top of a rhinoceros.

The rhino jumped up
with a terrible snort,
and Little Hippo ran.

He ran for a long, long time.
Finally he sank to the ground
in a little heap.

"Whoof. I can't run any more."

Just then the chameleon
put his head out of his house.

"Why, hello, Little Hippo,"
he said. "What are you doing here?"

"I'm lost," said Little Hippo.

"You're lost?" said the chameleon,
smiling. "Follow me!"

He led Little Hippo
to the top of a small hill.
"Now look, Little Hippo!"
And there right below him was Big Charles.
He and all the other hippos
were looking for something.

"Little Hippo, come out," they called, pushing through the grass.

"Come out, come out, wherever you are!" they shouted, peering under rocks.

But not one of them thought of looking up.

Little Hippo laughed and laughed.

"They'll never find me here,"
he said. "They don't see me
even though I'm in plain sight!"

"Home free! Home free!"
Little Hippo shouted
as he raced up to Big Charles.

All the big hippos were so glad
to see him that they bellowed
and stamped their hoofs.

"Where did you hide, Little Hippo?
We looked everywhere,"
said Big Charles.

But Little Hippo didn't tell.
He just smiled, because he knew
that the big hippos would always look
everywhere but up.
And he never told anyone
about his secret hiding place
where he could be alone,
but not too alone.

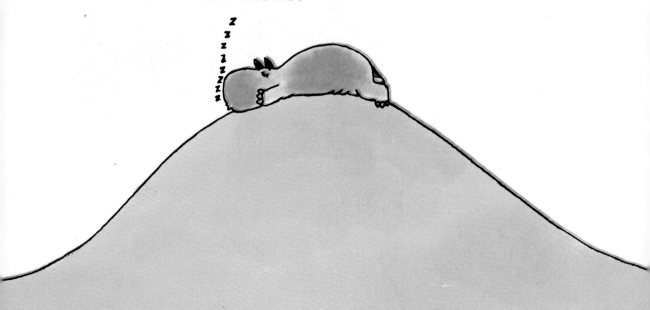

PICTURE DICTIONARY

Aa

animals

apartment house

Bb

bed

boy

137

Cc   cat

clothes

Dd   dime

Ee   eight

8

Ff   five

5

flower

four

fox

Gg giant

girl

Hh hen

Ii in

Jj

jay

Kk

king

Ll

legs

lion

Mm

meat

Nn

nine

140

Oo   owl

Pp   pig

Qq   quiet

Rr   raccoon

riding

Ss   seven

six

squirrel

stick

Tt ten

three

toys

Uu

umbrella

Vv

vegetables

Ww

witch

woodpecker

Xx

Yy

yellow

Zz

zebra

Series format, unit openers, Just for Fun pages, and covers designed by PUBLISHERS GRAPHICS.

Illustrations by: Erik Anderson, pp. 21–25, 74–75; Lloyd Birmingham, pp. 137–143; Ron Bosc, pp. 10–11; Marc Brown, pp. 52–58; Creative Photographers, pp. 63–72; Ray Cruz, pp. 32–40; Randall Enos, pp. 42–43, 103–104; Tom Garcia, pp. 16–20, 76–82; Leigh Grant, pp. 51, 106–116; Marylin Hafner, pp. 12–15, 44–50; Paul Harvey, pp. 60–61, 119–136; Sandy Kossin, pp. 27–31, 98–102; Susan Swan, pp. 91–97; Joe Veno, pp. 85–89.

Every care has been taken to trace the ownership and to locate the copyright holder of every selection included. If any errors or omissions have accidentally occurred, they will be corrected in subsequent printings, provided notification is sent to the publisher.

UNIT 2
Maytime Magic: Used by permission of the author, Mabel Watts.

UNIT 3
On the Ning Nang Nong: From SILLY VERSES FOR KIDS, by Spike Milligan. Reprinted by permission of Dennis Dobson, Publishers, London.

UNIT 4
The Secret Hiding Place: Reprinted by permission of The World Publishing Company from SECRET HIDING PLACE, by Rainey Bennett. Copyright © 1960 by Rainey Bennett.

2   3   4   5   6   7   8   9   10